THIS JOURNAL BELONGS TO

_____

YOUR LIFE IS YOURS. IT BELONGS TO YOU.

YOU ARE NOT REQUIRED TO CHECK IN WITH THE AGENTS AND GUARDIANS OF CULTURAL CENTRAL COMMAND BEFORE YOU DECIDE WHAT YOU NEED TO DO WITH YOUR LIFE. IT IS NOT THEIRS. IT DOES NOT BELONG TO THEM. NO MATTER WHAT THEY SAY, NO MATTER WHAT THE SHAPE OF YOUR JOURNEY MAY BE, YOU ARE ALLOWED TO MOVE EVER DEEPER INTO YOUR LIFE. THE OPERATIVE TRUTH HERE IS THAT IT IS YOURS.

IT'S YOURS.
IT'S YOURS.
IT'S YOURS.

—ELIZABETH GILBERT

It's yours.

It's yours.

It's yours.

It's yours.

It's yours.

It's yours.

It's yours.

It's yours.

It's yours.

It's yours.

It's yours.

It's yours.

It's yours.

It's yours.

It's yours.

It's yours.

It's yours.

It's yours.

It's yours.

It's yours.

It's yours.

It's yours.

It's yours.

It's yours.

It's yours.

It's yours.

It's yours.

It's yours.

It's yours.

It's yours.

It's yours.

It's yours.

It's yours.

It's yours.

It's yours.

It's yours.

It's yours.

It's yours.

It's yours.

It's yours.

It's yours.

It's yours.

It's yours.

It's yours.

It's yours.

It's yours.

It's yours.

It's yours.

It's yours.

It's yours.

It's yours.

It's yours.

It's yours.

It's yours.

It's yours.

It's yours.

It's yours.

It's yours.

It's yours.

It's yours.

It's yours.

It's yours.

It's yours.

It's yours.

It's yours.

It's yours.

It's yours.

It's yours.

It's yours.

It's yours.

It's yours.

It's yours.

It's yours.

It's yours.

It's yours.

It's yours.

It's yours.

It's yours.

It's yours.

It's yours.

It's yours.

It's yours.

It's yours.

It's yours.

It's yours.

It's yours.

It's yours.

It's yours.

It's yours.

It's yours.

It's yours.

It's yours.

It's yours.

It's yours.

It's yours.

It's yours.

It's yours.

It's yours.

It's yours.

It's yours.

It's yours.

It's yours.

It's yours.

It's yours.

It's yours.

It's yours.

It's yours.

It's yours.

It's yours.

It's yours.

It's yours.

It's yours.

It's yours.

It's yours.

It's yours.

It's yours.

It's yours.

It's yours.

It's yours.

It's yours.

It's yours.

It's yours.

It's yours.

It's yours.

It's yours.

It's yours.

It's yours.

It's yours.

It's yours.

It's yours.

It's yours.

It's yours.

It's yours.

It's yours.

It's yours.

It's yours.

It's yours.

It's yours.

It's yours.

It's yours.

It's yours.

It's yours.

It's yours.

It's yours.

It's yours.

It's yours.

It's yours.

It's yours.

It's yours.

It's yours.

It's yours.

It's yours.

It's yours.

It's yours.

It's yours.

It's yours.

It's yours.

It's yours.

It's yours.